God and You

Unlock the heart of the Christian message

God and You

Unlock the heart of the Christian message

Six discussions on Romans 1 - 5

Pete and Anne Woodcock

God and You
Unlock the heart of the Christian message
© Pete and Anne Woodcock/The Good Book Company

Published by
The Good Book Company
Tel (UK): 0333 123 0880
International: +44 (0) 208 942 0880
Email: info@thegoodbook.co.uk

An electronic leader's guide for *God and You* is available for purchase
and download from any of the websites below.

Websites
UK: www.thegoodbook.co.uk
N America: www.thegoodbook.com
Australia: www.thegoodbook.com.au
New Zealand: www.thegoodbook.co.nz

Design by André Parker

ISBN: 9781909919303
Printed in the Czech Republic

Read this first!

Ask the average person in the street: "What's Christianity all about?" or: "What is a Christian?"—and you'll probably get answers like "Believing in God" or "Someone who tries to live a good life". Most people assume that Christians live (or claim to live) good lives, following rules taught by Jesus. Most people think becoming a Christian is too difficult or makes you a hypocrite. Most people have missed what real Christianity is…

That's why *God and You* has been written. Just six one-hour sessions introduce you to the heart of the Christian good news, as recorded in the Bible and taught throughout the history of the Christian church. The course (originally called "Scripture Under Scrutiny") was designed for Australian university students with no church background or Bible knowledge. But it has been developed and expanded for use with people of all ages and backgrounds.

Maybe this is the first time you have ever studied the Bible. Perhaps you've never studied any book before. Don't worry—there are no exams to pass or fail, and no one is trying to "catch you out". *God and You* aims simply to help you understand the Christian good news.

We will look at part of Paul's letter to Christians in Rome—the book called Romans in the New Testament section of the Bible. Paul was a top Jewish rabbi who became the most famous leader of the early Christian church. In Romans he summarises the Christian message—in fact, the message of the whole Bible.

In each session there are Bible passages to read and questions to discuss:

> ❯ Most questions ask you what the Bible passage says. This collection of ancient documents, written over hundreds of years and by many different writers, reads like one book by a single author. Which is exactly what the Bible claims—that it is the word of God.

> ❯ **Think about it:** These questions ask if what the Bible says is true. How does it fit with what we see in the world? If the Bible really is God's word, what it says must be true and make sense even today.

> ❯ **Ask yourself:** These questions ask: "If this is true, then what should I do?" If God is speaking, we should be listening and ready to act on what he says.

We hope that *God and You* will be a real eye-opener and help you to see that the message of Jesus Christ is truly fantastic good news—for our world, for you, for today.

Pete & Anne

Contents

Says who?

❯ God has spoken clearly in the Bible, which tells us about Jesus Christ.

❯ This message is good news—where we learn that we need God's power to save us.

1. *Imagine you go into the home of someone you know nothing about.*

   a. By looking at the contents and condition of their home, what can (and can't) you find out about them?

   b. What added dimension would come from a personal letter written by this person to you?

At the beginning of his letter to the Christians in Rome (chapter 1, verses 1-17), Paul sets out:

- ❯ who he is—an apostle.
- ❯ what he does—he is "set apart for the gospel of God" and he calls non-Jewish people to trust, obey and belong to Jesus Christ.
- ❯ a summary of the gospel (the good news) of God.
- ❯ his love for the Christians in Rome.
- ❯ why he wants to visit Rome.

We will focus on what Paul says about God's message. We'll find out how people like us can know about God, what we can know about him, and what effect that has on our lives.

BIBLE EXTRACT

Romans, chapter 1, verses 1-6 and 14-20

Read this extract from the Bible, and use it to answer the following questions.

[1]Paul, a servant of Christ Jesus, called to be an apostle and set apart for the gospel of God—[2]the gospel he promised beforehand through his prophets in the Holy Scriptures [3]regarding his Son, who as to his earthly life was a descendant of David, [4]and who through the Spirit of holiness was appointed the Son of God in power by his resurrection from the dead: Jesus Christ our Lord. [5]Through him we received grace and apostleship to call all the Gentiles to the obedience that comes from faith for his name's sake. [6]And you also are among those Gentiles who are called to belong to Jesus Christ …

[14]I am a debtor both to Greeks and non-Greeks, both to the wise and the foolish. [15]That is why I am so eager to preach the gospel also to you who are in Rome. [16]For I am not ashamed of the gospel, because it is the power of God that brings salvation to everyone who believes: first to the Jew, then to the Gentile. [17]For in the gospel the righteousness of God is revealed—a righteousness that is by faith from first to last, just as it is written: "The righteous will live by faith."

[18]The wrath of God is being revealed from heaven against all the wickedness of people, who suppress the truth by their wickedness, [19]since what may be known about God is plain to them. [20]For since the creation of

the world God's invisible qualities—his eternal power and divine nature—have been clearly seen, being understood from what has been made, so that people are without excuse.

DICTIONARY

apostle (v 1): *someone who knew all about the life and teaching of Jesus first-hand and was especially chosen by Jesus to teach.*

gospel (v 1): *good news from God.*

prophet (v 2): *someone who brings God's message.*

Holy Scriptures (v 2): *the message of God in written form.*

David (v 3): *Israel's greatest king. God promised that he would have a descendant who would rule for ever.*

the Spirit of holiness (v 4): *the Holy Spirit, who is the third person of the Trinity (the one true God is a Trinity of three persons), with the Father, and the Son, Jesus Christ. The Holy Spirit is equal to the Father and the Son. He is also called the Spirit of God/Christ.*

Gentile (v 5): *anyone who isn't a Jew.*

righteousness (v 17): *what is right in God's eyes.*

wrath (v 18): *right and fierce anger.*

2. *According to Paul, what can people know about God? How do they find out about him (v 19-20)?*

   • *Look back to question 1. Is this like (a) or (b)?*

3. *In verse 1 Paul mentions the gospel (good news) of God. How has God communicated this message to us (v 2)?*

• *Look back to question 1. Is this like (a) or (b)?*

The words of the prophets are found in the part of the Bible we now call the "Old Testament". The words of witnesses of Jesus, and apostles like Paul, have also been written down, and are found in the "New Testament". The whole Bible is like a letter written to us by God.

4. *Look at verses 2-5 and 16-17. Summarise:*

   a. who God's message is for.

   b. its central themes.

c. its effect on people's lives.

Paul claims to speak with the authority of God—this message is not his own idea. He calls it "the gospel of God" (v 1) and "the gospel of his Son" (see v 9 below). Paul says that he is not a free agent—he calls himself "a servant of Christ Jesus" (v 1), and of God (see v 9 below). He serves them by teaching and spreading their good news.

BIBLE EXTRACT

Romans, chapter 1, verse 9

God, whom I serve in my spirit in preaching the gospel of his Son, is my witness how constantly I remember you.

5. *Think about it:*

What does God want us to know now? And where do we find this message?

6. *Ask yourself:*

In what ways might I need to change my view of the Bible? And of Jesus?

7. *How does Paul view the gospel of God?*

People have many ideas of how God speaks today (dreams, coincidences, voices in our heads), and of what he speaks about (usually guidance for decisions about jobs, relationships, where to live, etc). But Paul is clear: the key thing God wants us to know about is his Son, Jesus Christ. Paul points us to the writings of the prophets (Old Testament) and the teaching of himself and the other apostles (New Testament).

The Bible is where we learn that we need God's power to save us. If we don't find out what the Bible says, or if we read it for other "messages", we will never hear God's message to us.

8. *What do people do with the truth of God (v 18)? Why?*

9. *Think about it:*

In what ways do people today "suppress the truth" about God?

10. *Ask yourself:*

In what ways am I a "suppressor of the truth" about God?

What do I need to do in order to be a hearer of the truth about God?

SUMMARY

God has spoken to our world. He has shown us the truth about himself...

❯ in creation...

❯ but above all through Jesus Christ, his Son, as recorded in the Bible.

We need to listen to God by discovering what the Bible says.

BEFORE THE NEXT SESSION

❯ Read Romans chapter 1 v 18 to chapter 2 v 1.

❯ Think about what is wrong with our world and why.

❯ What do you learn about God that is new or surprising?

What in the world are we doing?

> Everyone is a sinner.

> God is rightly angry at our sin.

Last session we discovered that God has spoken to all of us in this world. The apostle Paul refers to this message as the gospel, or "good news". However, he is about to tell us some very bad news. Paul is like a doctor—he needs to tell us what our problem is before he can give the good news of the remedy.

1. *Why is it that sex, scandal and crime always sell books, papers and magazines, and attract the highest viewing rates on television?*

Imagine you're an original reader of Paul's letter. One very important fact about you would be whether you were a Jew (an ethnic minority in Rome) or a Gentile (a non-Jew—Roman, Greek or other).

The Jews had thousands of years of history, recorded in the Old Testament. They had always believed that their nation—Israel—alone knew and understood the one true God. They believed that by following the Law of Moses and the traditions of their elders, they lived in a way that pleased God and would be rewarded by him. Since all other ethnic groups were pagan—worshipping many gods by means of man-made idols—Jews considered it was not fitting even to eat with Gentiles, whom they regarded as worthless as dogs.

BIBLE EXTRACT

Romans, chapter 1, verses 18-32

Read this extract from the Bible, and use it to answer the following questions.

[18]The wrath of God is being revealed from heaven against all the godlessness and wickedness of people, who suppress the truth by their wickedness, [19]since what may be known about God is plain to them, because God has made it plain to them. [20]For since the creation of the world God's invisible qualities—his eternal power and divine nature—have been clearly seen, being understood from what has been made, so that people are without excuse.

[21]For although they knew God, they neither glorified him as God nor gave thanks to him, but their thinking became futile and their foolish hearts were darkened. [22]Although they claimed to be wise, they became fools [23]and exchanged the glory of the immortal God for images made to look like a mortal human being and birds and animals and reptiles.

[24]Therefore God gave them over in the sinful desires of their hearts to sexual impurity for the degrading of their bodies with one another. [25]They exchanged the truth about God for a lie, and worshipped and served created things rather than the Creator—who is for ever praised. Amen.

[26]Because of this, God gave them over to shameful lusts. Even their women exchanged natural sexual relations for unnatural ones. [27]In the same way the men also abandoned natural relations with women and were inflamed with lust for one another. Men committed shameful acts with

other men, and received in themselves the due penalty for their error.

²⁸Furthermore, just as they did not think it worth while to retain the knowledge of God, so God gave them over to a depraved mind, so that they do what ought not to be done. ²⁹They have become filled with every kind of wickedness, evil, greed and depravity. They are full of envy, murder, strife, deceit and malice. They are gossips, ³⁰slanderers, God-haters, insolent, arrogant and boastful; they invent ways of doing evil; they disobey their parents; ³¹they have no understanding, no fidelity, no love, no mercy. ³²Although they know God's righteous decree that those who do such things deserve death, they not only continue to do these very things but also approve of those who practise them.

DICTIONARY

wrath (v 18): *right and fierce anger.*

2. *What do we learn about the behaviour and character of the people described in chapter 1?*

It would have been clear to Paul's readers that this was a description of Roman society. The Romans worshipped many idol gods, and the imperial capital was notorious for destructive behaviour.

3. *What do you think about these people? Would you like them as neighbours?*

4. *Who decides what is right and wrong? Look at verses 18, 21-23 and 32.*

5. *Look at verses 24, 26 and 28. What does God do about these people? What is surprising about this?*

Often we think that if God is angry at something we do, he will stop it. But Paul says that God gives us over to these things (lets us do them), not because of a "relaxed" attitude, but to show his wrath. Never think that because God hasn't stopped you from doing something, he is ok with that behaviour.

6. *Can anyone plead ignorance about God? Why or why not?*

Romans, chapter 2, verse 1

Read this extract from the Bible, and use it to answer the following questions.

> You, therefore, have no excuse, you who pass judgment on someone else, for at whatever point you judge another, you are condemning yourself, because you who pass judgment do the same things.

DICTIONARY

judgment: *condemnation (not discernment).*

7. *Who is Paul addressing here?*

- *In what way are these people different from those in chapter 1? In what way are they the same?*

8. *Are we judgmental? (Look again at question 3.)*

• *Why should we not be judgmental?*

9. Think about it:

In what ways are people today judgmental?

10. Ask yourself:

What have I learned about myself from these verses?

We now fast-forward to chapter 3, where Paul gives his conclusion about what people are doing in this world—and it's devastating, especially for his Jewish readers. Paul quotes from several writers of the Jewish Scriptures themselves (the Old Testament) to prove his point.

Romans, chapter 3, verses 9-18

Read this extract from the Bible, and use it to answer the following questions.

⁹What shall we conclude then? Do we [ie: we Jews] have any advantage? Not at all! For we have already made the charge that Jews and Gentiles alike are all under the power of sin. ¹⁰As it is written: "There is no one righteous, not even one; ¹¹there is no one who understands; there is no one who seeks God. ¹²All have turned away, they have together become worthless; there is no one who does good, not even one." ¹³"Their throats are open graves; their tongues practise deceit." "The poison of vipers is on their lips." ¹⁴"Their mouths are full of cursing and bitterness." ¹⁵"Their feet are swift to shed blood; ¹⁶ruin and misery mark their ways, ¹⁷and the way of peace they do not know." ¹⁸"There is no fear of God before their eyes."

DICTIONARY

Gentile (v 9): *anyone who isn't a Jew.*

sin (v 9): *rebellion against God.*

righteous (v 10): *right in God's eyes.*

fear (v 18): *great honour and respect.*

11. What conclusion does Paul reach in these verses?

- *Look at the medical check-up that he carries out in verses 13-18. What is the diagnosis for our mouth, feet and eyes?*

12. Think about it:

Is this true of the world? For example...

- *do people worship created things instead of the Creator (1 v 25)?*

- *is everyone a liar (3 v 13)?*

- *is Paul right when he says that everyone is "under the power of sin" (3 v 9)?*

13. *Ask yourself:*

What does this say about me?

What follows about my standing with God?

14. *Review:*

From what we have learned in this session, how can sinful people ever be acceptable to the perfect God?

SUMMARY

- ❯ **Session 1:** God has spoken to our world but we suppress that truth.
- ❯ **This session:** We refuse to treat God as God; we turn to idolatry; we try to decide what is right and wrong; our lives show we are full of sin.
- ❯ Even those of us who try to be "good" fail; we judge others and end up judging ourselves because we are no different.
- ❯ God is showing his anger at our sin.

BEFORE THE NEXT SESSION

❯ Read Romans chapter 2, verses 1-16.

❯ Think about whether there is any such thing as justice, and if so, where it can be found.

❯ What do you learn about God that is new or surprising?

What in the world is God doing?

❯ God is our righteous Judge.

❯ One day he will judge all sin.

Last session we learned that:

❯ suppressing the truth about God leads to all the evil and wrong behaviour we see in our world.

❯ when we—thinking we're better—find fault with others, we judge ourselves guilty because we do the same bad things.

❯ everyone is guilty of sin.

❯ God is showing his anger at our sin by letting us do what we want.

Now the bad news of the last session gets worse! God's anger against us now is not his final word on the matter...

1. *Do you agree that people should be held responsible and accountable for their actions?*

- *What would the world be like if people were not held accountable in any way?*

In this part of his letter, Paul speaks directly to people who have been brought up as God-fearing Jews. They condemn the Gentiles around them for their idolatry and wicked lifestyles, never imagining that they themselves are equally guilty and so also under God's wrath.

BIBLE EXTRACT

Romans, chapter 2, verses 1-16

Read this extract from the Bible, and use it to answer the following questions.

[1]You, therefore, have no excuse, you who pass judgment on someone else, for at whatever point you judge another, you are condemning yourself, because you who pass judgment do the same things. [2]Now we know that God's judgment against those who do such things is based on truth. [3]So when you, a mere human being, pass judgment on them and yet do the same things, do you think you will escape God's judgment? [4]Or do you show contempt for the riches of his kindness, forbearance and patience, not realising that God's kindness is intended to lead you to repentance?

[5]But because of your stubbornness and your unrepentant heart, you are storing up wrath against yourself for the day of God's wrath, when his righteous judgment will be revealed. [6]God "will repay each person according to what they have done." [7]To those who by persistence in doing good seek glory, honour and immortality, he will give eternal life. [8]But for those who are self-seeking and who reject the truth and follow evil, there will be wrath and anger. [9]There will be trouble and distress for every human being who does evil: first for the Jew, then for the Gentile; [10]but glory, honour and peace for everyone who does good: first for the Jew, then for the Gentile. [11]For God does not show favouritism.

¹²All who sin apart from the law will also perish apart from the law, and all who sin under the law will be judged by the law. ¹³For it is not those who hear the law who are righteous in God's sight, but it is those who obey the law who will be declared righteous. ¹⁴(Indeed, when Gentiles, who do not have the law, do by nature things required by the law, they are a law for themselves, even though they do not have the law. ¹⁵They show that the requirements of the law are written on their hearts, their consciences also bearing witness, and their thoughts sometimes accusing them and at other times even defending them.) ¹⁶This will take place on the day when God judges people's secrets through Jesus Christ, as my gospel declares.

DICTIONARY

pass judgment (v 1): *condemn.*

repentance (v 4): *turning away from sin and back to God.*

the law (v 12): *the rules that God gave to the people of Israel (the Jews).*

2. *God is already showing his anger against sin now (1 v 18, 24, 26, 28). But what will he do in the future?*

3. *Find out how God will judge., and write down what you discover.*

• What will he look at (v 6, 16)?

• What standards will he judge by (v 7, 8 and 13)?

• Who will do the judging (v 16)?

• How will he show fairness both to the knowledgeable (eg: Jews) and the ignorant (eg: Gentiles) (v 12-15)?

4. **Think about it:**

   Why do you think God will judge us? Why is he angry about our sinfulness?

Why is this teaching about God's judgment so unpopular today? Because it opposes popular views on some important issues:

❯ There's not one standard of right and wrong for everyone; we believe each person can do what's right for them.

❯ It's offensive that someone else—even God—can tell us what to do or not do.

❯ The idea of guilt is unpopular; instead we talk about people acting "inappropriately" because they are victims of their DNA, upbringing or circumstances.

❯ We talk about rehabilitating offenders, protecting the public and deterring crime, but the idea of deserved retribution is disregarded.

But there's a bigger issue to think about…

5. *Think about it:*

• *How common is the desire for justice in our world?*

• *Why can true justice never be achieved in this life?*

• *If there is such a thing as justice in the universe, who can give it and how?*

Re-read Romans chapter 2, verses 5-11 to help you answer the following questions.

6. *What will happen to the righteous? What kind of people are they?*

7. *What will happen to the unrighteous? What kind of people are they?*

Last session we saw Paul conclude that everyone is a sinner. But now he seems to say that good people will go to heaven (v 7 and 10). Is he contradicting himself?

We need to ask:

a. Who qualifies here for eternal life?

❯ Those who do "good" (v 7): God decides what is good. Before we label ourselves as good, we need to know what God thinks is good.

❯ Those who "persist" in doing good (v 7): doing something good occasionally is not enough for eternal life.

❯ Those who seek "glory, honour and immortality" (v 7): The word "immortality" tells us that we can seek these things only from God. It's not just a matter of doing good things but of being in a right relationship with God.

b. Who doesn't qualify?

❯ "Those who are self-seeking and who reject the truth and follow evil" (v 8)—exactly the route which, as we saw in Session 2, everyone takes.

Paul is saying here that God will give eternal life to anyone who qualifies. But in fact that's only one person—Jesus Christ. It's not good news for the rest of us.

8. Think about it:

Can God show justice without judgment? Why or why not?

The next question is probably the most important one in this course.

9. Ask yourself:

Do I want God to treat me with justice?

 • *If yes, that will mean...*

 • *If no, that will mean...*

10. Review:

From what we have learned so far, how can anyone be saved from God's wrath and judgment?

SUMMARY

❯ **Session 1:** We are all guilty of sin.

❯ **Session 2:** There is justice in the universe only because one day God will punish all the wrong things that have been done.

❯ God will punish me for the wrong things I have done and for the wrong secret thoughts that I have had.

❯ This session: So far, the only way to be acceptable to the perfect God is "by persistence in doing good [to] seek glory, honour and immortality". But no one, except Jesus Christ, has done that.

BEFORE THE NEXT SESSION

❯ Read Romans chapter 2, verses 17-29.

❯ Think about how people might try to respond to the teaching in this session—that one day God will judge everyone.

❯ What do you learn about the Jews (who were known as "God's people") that is new or surprising?

What can religion do?

> ❯ Our biggest problem is that we have all sinned, and one day God will judge all sin.

> ❯ No religion—not even God's law— can solve the problem of sin.

Last session we learned that there is justice in the universe only because one day God will punish all the wrong things that have been done. God's judgment is good news because one day perfect justice will be done. But it is also bad news because each one of us is going to be judged by God. Our problem is that we want justice, but we don't want judgment. So how can we escape God's punishment—how can we become acceptable to the perfectly just God?

1. *Our biggest problem is that we have all sinned, and one day God will judge all sin. Many people think religion can help—in what way?*

If you were a Jew, the law of Moses would be central to your way of life. In ancient times, this law was given by God to the people of Israel (the Jews), through their leader Moses, after rescue from slavery in Egypt. (You can read about this in the Old Testament book of Exodus.)

The most famous part of this law was the Ten Commandments, but many other rules covered all areas of life, including: religion (sacrifices and gifts to God, priests, places of worship, special celebrations); social matters (marriage, employers, debt); lifestyle matters (diet, clothing, diseases); and crime and punishment. (These laws are in the Old Testament books of Exodus, Leviticus and Deuteronomy.)

The Jews were given this law so they could show the other nations how great God is and what he does for his people. Because of their law, Jews believed they were a "light for the Gentiles".

BIBLE EXTRACT

Romans, chapter 2, verses 17-29

Read this extract from the Bible, and use it to answer the following questions.

[17]Now you, if you call yourself a Jew; if you rely on the law and boast in God; [18]if you know his will and approve of what is superior because you are instructed by the law; [19]if you are convinced that you are a guide for the blind, a light for those who are in the dark, [20]an instructor of the foolish, a teacher of little children, because you have in the law the embodiment of knowledge and truth—[21]you, then, who teach others, do you not teach yourself? You who preach against stealing, do you steal? [22]You who say that people should not commit adultery, do you commit adultery? You who abhor idols, do you rob temples? [23]You who boast in the law, do you dishonour God by breaking the law? [24]As it is written: "God's name is blasphemed among the Gentiles because of you."

[25]Circumcision has value if you observe the law, but if you break the law, you have become as though you had not been circumcised. [26]So then, if those who are not circumcised keep the law's requirements, will they not be regarded as though they were circumcised? [27]The one who is not circumcised physically and yet obeys the law will condemn you who, even though you have the written code and circumcision, are a law-breaker.

²⁸A person is not a Jew who is one only outwardly, nor is circumcision merely outward and physical. ²⁹No, a person is a Jew who is one inwardly; and circumcision is circumcision of the heart, by the Spirit, not by the written code. Such a person's praise is not from other people, but from God.

DICTIONARY

the law (v 17): *God's rules for the people of Israel (the Jews).*

blaspheme (v 24): *dishonour the name of God.*

circumcision (v 25): *a minor genital operation performed on Jewish boys as a sign that they were God's people. It was commanded in the law.*

the written code (v 29): *another term for God's law.*

2. *What does God require of those who have the law?*

• *Did the religious people, the Jews, meet that requirement?*

3. *What was their attitude to the law? Note the verbs used in verses 17, 18, 21 and 23.*

• Was their devotion good enough for God?

4. Who is the condemned law-breaker in verse 27?

• What would Paul's Jewish readers have made of this?

5. Did circumcision make a person right with God?

6. **Think about it:**

In our culture, what religious practices have replaced Jewish law and circumcision as the way by which people think they can be acceptable to God?

7. *Ask yourself:*

In what ways might I need to change my view of righteousness (= goodness that is good enough for God)?

Do you remember Paul's conclusion that all of us, Jews and Gentiles alike, are under the power of sin? We looked at that part of Romans chapter 3 (verses 9-18) in Session 2. At the end of that passage we now find Paul's conclusion about the purpose of Israel's law.

BIBLE EXTRACT

Romans, chapter 3, verses 19-20

Read this extract from the Bible, and use it to answer the following questions.

> [19]Now we know that whatever the law says, it says to those who are under the law, so that every mouth may be silenced and the whole world held accountable to God. [20]Therefore no one will be declared righteous in God's sight by the works of the law; rather, through the law we become conscious of our sin.

DICTIONARY

sin (v 20): *rebellion against God.*

8. *Will anyone be declared righteous by "the works of the law" (= doing what the law says)?*

9. What does the law achieve?

10. Whose law is Paul talking about?

   • Is there anything wrong with this law?

11. **Think about it:**

   Can any religious practices (keeping religious rules, performing rituals, having experiences) get you closer to God?

   • Or solve the problem of sin?

12. Ask yourself:

What am I trusting in to reconcile me to God? Am I trusting in laws or rituals or experiences to make me righteous?

• *If so, what are the implications?*

13. Review:

From what we have learned so far, is it possible for anyone to be righteous?

SUMMARY

❯ **Sessions 2 and 3:** The biggest problem for each one of us is that we have sinned, and so one day God will judge and punish us.

❯ **This session:** No religious practices (rules, rituals or experiences) can solve this problem.

❯ Even God's law can't make us right with him, because no one keeps God's law.

❯ God's law only shows us our sin.

BEFORE THE NEXT SESSION

- Read Romans 3 v 21-31.
- From these verses, think about what God has done, what Jesus has done and what we need to do.
- What do you learn about the Christian message (the good news of Jesus Christ) that is new or surprising?

God's gift

❯ Only the death of Jesus can save us from our sin and God's judgment against us.

1. *Who will be declared righteous in God's sight, according to Paul? (Look at Romans 3 v 9, 10 on p 23; and 3 v 20 on p 39.)*

Last session we learned how our biggest problem is that...

❯ each of us has sinned...

❯ so one day God will judge and punish each of us...

❯ and religion can't help us solve this problem.

❯ Even God's law can't help us; it only shows us our sin.

If even God's law can't help us to become righteous and save us from God's judgment, what hope is there for us? No hope!

We have reached the point where we should realise that there is NOTHING we can do to save ourselves. But the night seems darkest just before dawn. Finally, we are ready to hear the good news.

2. *Imagine that you unexpectedly receive a very generous and much-needed gift, given purely out of love and kindness. How do you feel towards the giver?*

• *How is this different to receiving a payment, right or reward?*

• *Why do people sometimes dislike receiving gifts?*

BIBLE EXTRACT

Romans, chapter 3, verses 21-31

Note: This course doesn't include Romans 3 v 1-8 (the advantage of being a Jew, in light of the fact that Jews are just as much sinners as non-Jews).

Read this extract from the Bible, and use it to answer the following questions.

[21]But now apart from the law the righteousness of God has been made known, to which the Law and the Prophets testify. [22]This righteousness is given though faith in Jesus Christ to all who believe. There is no difference between Jew and Gentile, [23]for all have sinned and fall short of the glory of God, [24]and all are justified freely by his grace through the redemption that came by Christ Jesus. [25]God presented Christ as a sacrifice of atonement, through the shedding of his blood—to be received by faith. He did this to demonstrate his righteousness, because in his forbearance he had left the sins committed beforehand unpunished [26]—he did it to demonstrate his righteousness at the present time, so as to be just and the one who justifies those who have faith in Jesus.

[27]Where, then, is boasting? It is excluded. Because of what law? The law that requires works? No, because of the "law" that requires faith. [28]For we maintain that a person is justified by faith apart from the works of the law. [29]Or is God the God of Jews only? Is he not the God of the Gentiles too? Yes, of Gentiles too, [30]since there is only one God, who will justify the circumcised by faith and the uncircumcised through that same faith. [31]Do we, then, nullify the law by this faith? Not at all! Rather, we uphold the law.

DICTIONARY

the Law and the Prophets (v 21): *God's word to Israel, now two major sections of the Old Testament.*

faith (v 22): *trust, dependence.*

justified (v 24): *declared right.*

grace (v 24): *undeserved kindness.*

redemption (v 24): *paying the price to free a slave.*

atonement (v 25): *making amends for wrong, leading to reconciliation.*

forbearance (v 25): *mercy to sinners.*

works (v 27): *good things done to earn a reward from God.*

the circumcised / the uncircumcised (v 30): *Jews / Gentiles.*

3. *Based on verses 21-26, write out in your own words how someone can become right with God. (Use the following questions, and dictionary (p 43), to help you.)*

- *v 21-22: What do people need to be reconciled to God? Where does it come from and where does it not come from? How do we get this?*

- *v 24: Look at the word "justified". What does God think of people who have faith in Jesus Christ?*

- *v 24: Look at the words "freely by his grace". Do we have a right to expect that God must do this? Do we earn it or pay for it?*

- *v 24: Look at the word "redemption". What price did Jesus Christ pay? What "slavery" does this free us from?*

- *v 25: Look at the words "sacrifice of atonement". What was the significance of Jesus' death?*

• *v 25: What do we need to trust in to get right with God?*

Now write in your own words here:

When we put our faith in Jesus, how does his death pay for our sin?

- ❯ **His death justifies us:** We are no longer "guilty" in God's eyes because the punishment for our sin has already been paid when Jesus died.
- ❯ **His death redeems us:** Jesus suffered enough to pay the price needed to buy us out of our slavery to sin and its consequence—God's judgment.
- ❯ **His death is a sacrifice of atonement:** When Jesus died, God's right and just anger was directed onto him, in place of us, making it possible for us to be reconciled to God.

4. *How can the crucifixion of Jesus demonstrate God's justice (v 25)?*

5. *How can God be both merciful and just at the same time (v 25-26)?*

6. *Think about it:*

   Is there any other way in which God can show that he is both just and merciful?

7. *Think about it:*

   How does the good news of Jesus Christ fit with today's popular belief that there are many ways to God?

8. *Ask yourself:*

   In what ways might I need to change my views of other teachings about how we can be acceptable to God?

A true Christian is… someone who is convinced that Jesus Christ is the only way to God.

9. *Is this gift of righteousness from God deserved?*

10. *Who receives the gift, and how do they receive it?*

11. *Does a Christian (someone who has been made right with God through Jesus Christ) have any reason for boasting (verses 27-28)?*

• *Or for being judgmental?*

A true Christian is... someone who will always admit that they are a sinner, and readily accepts that they are worse than others.

12. *Think about it:*

Is anyone too sinful for God to forgive them? Why or why not?

A true Christian is... someone who accepts that even the most evil person can be forgiven by God if that person trusts in Jesus Christ to save them.

13. *Ask yourself:*

• *Am I too sinful to be acceptable to God based on my own goodness?*

• *Am I too sinful to be acceptable to God based on Jesus' death?*

• *Where does my faith (= trust) lie—in Jesus' death or in something else?*

• *What would it mean for me to put my faith in Jesus' death?*

You may now have reached the point where you understand the gospel of God. If you're ready to put your faith in Jesus Christ, and ask him to save you from your sin and God's judgment, all you need to do is to talk to God about it. In your own time and your own words, you can say a prayer like the one below. If you truly mean what you say to God, you can be confident that he will hear and answer your prayer.

> *Dear God,*
>
> *I know that I have lived as your enemy.*
>
> *Thank you that you love me anyway and sent Jesus to die on my behalf.*
>
> *Please forgive me and change me so that I may live with Jesus as my Lord.*

SUMMARY

❯ **Sessions 2 to 4:** There is nothing we can do to save ourselves from our sin and God's judgment against us. BUT…

❯ **This session:** God has a way to make people right with him—it's not by trying to keep his law but by faith in Jesus Christ and his death to save us.

❯ Jesus died as a sacrifice of atonement—he took the place of sinners and suffered God's penalty for sin so that the way is clear for sinners to be reconciled with God.

❯ If I trust in Jesus and what he did on the cross, God will decide that I am "not guilty" and I will not be punished on the day of judgment.

BEFORE THE NEXT SESSION

❯ Read Romans chapter 5, verses 1-11.

❯ From these verses, think about what changes when someone trusts in Jesus and his death on the cross to save them from God's judgment.

❯ What do you learn about the Christian life that is new or surprising?

Right with God

> ❯ Those who put their faith in Jesus Christ live a new, changed life, full of good gifts from God, both in this world and eternity.

In Session Four we saw Paul drop a bombshell for his readers: no one will be saved from God's judgment by trying to keep religious laws or performing religious rituals—not even Jews trying to keep God's law. We cannot be saved by anything that we do.

Last session we finally discovered the good news: God is both merciful and just—and God alone can make sinners righteous. We can only be saved by putting faith (= trust) in what Jesus has done for us. When this happens, nothing can ever be the same. In this session we will see what life is like for God's saved people—past, present and future.

1. *What is the most striking example of reconciliation that you have had with another person in your life, or know of in someone else's life? Or give an example from history.*

Romans, chapter 5, verses 1-11

Note: This course doesn't include Romans chapter 4 (Paul showing his Jewish readers that even Abraham, the "father of the Jews", was not righteous because of anything he had done but because he had faith—he "believed God").

Read this extract from the Bible, and use it to answer the following questions.

(Alternative translations are taken from the 1984 edition of the New International Version—see bold italics.)

¹Therefore, since we have been justified through faith, we have peace with God through our Lord Jesus Christ, ²through whom we have gained access by faith into this grace in which we now stand. And we boast/ ***rejoice*** in the hope of the glory of God. ³Not only so, but we also glory/ ***rejoice*** in our sufferings, because we know that suffering produces perseverance; ⁴perseverance, character; and character, hope. ⁵And hope does not put us to shame, because God's love has been poured into our hearts through the Holy Spirit, who has been given to us.

⁶You see, at just the right time, when we were still powerless, Christ died for the ungodly. ⁷Very rarely will anyone die for a righteous person, though for a good person someone might possibly dare to die. ⁸But God demonstrates his own love for us in this: while we were still sinners, Christ died for us.

⁹Since we have now been justified by his blood, how much more shall we be saved from God's wrath through him! ¹⁰For if, while we were God's enemies, we were reconciled to him through the death of his Son, how much more, having been reconciled, shall we be saved through his life! ¹¹Not only is this so, but we also boast/***rejoice*** in God through our Lord Jesus Christ, through whom we have now received reconciliation.

DICTIONARY

justified (v 1): *declared right.*

faith (v 1): *trust in or dependence on Jesus Christ.*

grace (v 2): *undeserved kindness.*

the Holy Spirit (v 5): *the third person of the Trinity (the one true God* *is a Trinity of three persons), along with the Father, and the Son, Jesus Christ. The Holy Spirit is equal to the Father and the Son. He is also called the Spirit of God/Christ/holiness.*

2. List the benefits of being a Christian mentioned in the passage.

    • In the past:

    • In the present:

    • In the future:

3. **Think about it:**

    What would it be like to be at peace with God? How would your thinking change? How would your life change?

A true Christian is… not someone who has "always been a Christian", but someone who has become a Christian and whose life has been changed by the good news of Jesus Christ.

4. *Ask yourself:*

   In my search for God, have I got to the stage where I can say I am at peace with him?

   • *Would I like to be reconciled to God?*

5. *How have Christians gained access to God's grace, so that now they can enjoy his love and kindness, instead of facing his wrath and judgment?*

6. *Does suffering in this life mean that people are not right with God? Why or why not?*

7. *Why do you think Christians are expected to suffer (v 3-5)?*

8. *How has God demonstrated his love (v 8)?*

• *So how do we know that God loves us even when we are suffering?*

9. *What will Christians be saved from (v 9)?*

10. *What assurances does Paul give us that the problem of sin really has been dealt with, and therefore Christians will be saved on the Day of Judgment? (See chapter 4, verse 25 below and compare 5 v 9-10 on p 54.)*

(See chapter 4, verse 25 below and compare 5 v 9-10 on p 54.)

BIBLE EXTRACT

Romans chapter 4, verse 25

[Jesus Christ] was delivered over to death for our sins and was raised to life for our justification.

11. ***Think about it:***

What right do Christians have to be sure that they are going to heaven, do you think?

A true Christian is… someone who is certain that they are going to heaven—because of what Jesus Christ has done for them.

12. *Ask yourself:*

Am I absolutely sure that when I die my body will be raised to enjoy eternal life with the God who loves me in his perfect new universe? Why or why not?

SUMMARY

❯ When someone trusts in Jesus and his death on the cross to save them from their sin and God's judgment, everything changes—nothing can ever be the same.

❯ In the present, Christians can have peace with God, joy even when they suffer, and hope for the future.

❯ For the future, Christians can be certain that they will be saved from God's judgment because Jesus' death paid for their sin; and Jesus' resurrection proved that God has accepted Jesus' payment on their behalf.

❯ Christians can always be confident of God's love, whatever their circumstances, because God has shown his love in sending Jesus to die for them.

WHAT NEXT?

Think about this course as a whole. What things are clearer in your understanding about the message of the Bible now? What questions do you still have?

Think about what to do next. There are a number of things you can now do:

❯ Re-read Romans 1 – 5.

❯ Look again through this book.

❯ Work out any question you still have and ask your group leader.

❯ Keep meeting with others to study the Bible and hear more about the good news of the gospel.

❯ Think about what is stopping you from following Jesus Christ. Ask yourself: *Why wouldn't I want to follow him?*